# The Fairy Glen School for Fairies:
# An Adventurous Journey

## By David Plested

It was a special day at the Fairy Glen School,
the class gathered round near the top waterfall.

"Today fairies we will take a trip to the Beach",
said the Elder Fairy eager to teach.

"The beach is a long way so we'll go slow and steady.
Stay close together and keep your wands at the ready".

The class grabbed their wands and walked down the slope,
the path was very narrow so they held onto the rope.

The Elder Fairy said "be careful, don't slip!",
so the fairies took care not to spoil their school trip.

Out from the bushes an almighty

'CROW CROW'

This was a sound
the fairies didn't know.

Flapping its wings flew a bright coloured pheasant.
"Gather round fairies I must make sure everyone's present".

"Quick fairies, you mustn't dwell!
We must work as a team if we want to cast this spell".

So the fairies held hands and working together,
cast the spell to become a fluffy feather.

The pheasant couldn't see the fairies hiding at all,
so the fairies fluttered down to the next waterfall.

"Down in the burn, the water runs fast,
we must stay where it is calm if we want to get past".

"You must all behave or we'll get swept away,
when we get to the beach you'll have time to play".

# 'Splish, Splash'

along swam a vole,
across the water from a little hole.

"Quick fairies, you have to hide!"
So with a                              and a

'Swoosh'    'Swish'

they turned into fish.

The water vole could no longer see them with ease,
so the fairies went on, into the trees.

"The trees here are tall, so keep an eye on the sky.
We don't know what's hiding, so hold your wands up high".

**'Boing, Flip'**

jumped a creature dressed in red,
"look out, a red squirrel!" the Elder Fairy said.

"Quick fairies, you have to hide!"

So with a        and a

**'Flap'        'Flick'**        they turned into a stick.

The squirrel couldn't see the fairies being hidden by their wand, so the fairies rolled on, down to the pond.

"The pond is very deep fairies, follow the rules".
So the fairies waded through the shallow water pools.

A duck flapped close and shouted,

'Quack,
Quack'

It was a shock to the fairies
and they all fell back.

"Quick fairies, you have to hide!"

So with a                    and a

'Shiver'  'Shake'

they became
a snowflake.

The duck couldn't see the fairies, so flew on over the ridge,
and the fairies floated on, down to the bridge.

The fairies had never travelled so far before
and were eager to travel further, closer to the shore.

# 'Scratch, Sniff'

A pine martin hid,
in some rocks down by the cliff.

"Quick fairies, you have to hide!"

So with a          and a

# 'Whistle' 'Wave'

they disappeared
into the cave.

As the fairies were out of the pine martins reach,
the fairies crept out and down to the beach.

The fairies travelled far without a moan or a groan,
but now on the beach surely they were alone.

"Look out fairies! It's a little girl" The Elder Fairy cried.
"Use what you have learnt so far to hide".

So the fairies grabbed their wands,
and with a              and a

'Twist' 'Twirl' they did all they could to
hide from this girl.

With a 'Zip' and a 'Zoom',
one became a mushroom.

With a 'Pip' and a 'Pop',
one became a rain drop.

With a 'Nod' and a 'Knock',
one turned into a rock.

With all their might and power,
one became a bright yellow flower.

The little girl knew the fairies were there,
the only problem was that she didn't know where.

She came equipped with a magnifying glass,
it would be only moments before she found the class.

"Don't worry fairies there is nothing to fear",
said the little girl as she came near.

She searched here and there,

on the ground                    and in the air.

She searched high and low,
until she found something aglow.

It was a fairy, or two, four, maybe more.

She shrieked with delight and gave the fairies a fright.

She meant harm to no-one, all she wanted was fun.

So slowly but surely they each crept out,
they knew she was friendly without a doubt.

With the sand in their toes and sun on their back,
they could play all day until the sky went black.

So they danced and they played,
they were no longer afraid.

Then along came a figure, tall and fearsome...

"Look out fairies!

It's my mum!".

David Plested is a writer, designer and illustrator from the Black Isle in the Highlands of Scotland. He studied architecture before specialising in visual communication. His work varies from mixed media models and paintings using traditional techniques to photography and digital imaging. David's passions have grown and developed as he is inspired by the Scottish landscapes, flora and fauna.

The Fairy Glen School for Fairies: An Adventurous Journey is set within the RSPB nature reserve, Fairy Glen, in Rosemarkie, Black Isle, Scotland. The book is designed to help engage younger audiences with their environment. All images, including the elements that make up the fairies themselves, were taken either within the Fairy Glen or in the surrounding areas.

dplested@dpi-illustration.com